LET'S VISIT
A Space Camp

by Edith Alston

photography by Michael Plunkett

Troll Associates

Library of Congress Cataloging-in-Publication Data

Alston, Edith.
    Let's visit a space camp / by Edith Alston; photography by
Michael Plunkett.
        p.   cm.
    Summary: Tours the Space and Rocket Center in Huntsville, Alabama,
describing exhibits, spacecraft, and activities at the space camp
where children can experience what space travel feels like and
participate in a simulated space shuttle mission.
    ISBN 0-8167-1743-5 (lib. bdg.)   ISBN 0-8167-1744-3 (pbk.)
    1. Astronautics—Juvenile literature.   [1. Astronautics.]
I. Plunkett, Michael, ill.   II. Title.
TL793.A48   1990
629.45—dc20   89-34373

Copyright © 1990 by Troll Associates, Mahwah, New Jersey

10 9 8 7 6 5 4 3 2 1

The author and the publisher wish to thank Phillip Gentry and The Space and Rocket Center and William
Anderson and the Marshall Space Flight Center for their generous assistance and cooperation, and to
acknowledge the following for their photographs: Glenn Baeske, p. 25; NASA, pgs. 3, 4, 7 (inset), 8, 9, 18 (inset), 19,
23 (left), 28 (inset), 31 (inset) and 32; and The Space and Rocket Center, pgs. 9, 20, and 23 (right).

Everybody dreams about going into space. But space is very different from earth. In space there is no air to breathe. There is not even an "up" and "down" as we know it! And there is very little gravity, so everything floats. Gravity is the force that keeps us on Earth. To go into space, we must first escape the Earth's gravity.

To escape the Earth's gravity, astronauts need a launch vehicle with powerful rocket engines. The forward force on a rocket as it burns fuel is called thrust. When the Saturn V launch vehicle pushed off for the moon, it used nearly eight million pounds of thrust! To find out more about taking a space trip, let's visit The Space and Rocket Center, in Huntsville, Alabama.

In the United States, the National Aeronautics and Space Administration (NASA) is in charge of space exploration. Many NASA rockets and launch vehicles are on view in Rocket Park at The Space and Rocket Center. The Saturn V is the biggest. With the Apollo spacecraft in place at the top, it was 363 feet high! Now, in the park, it lies in sections on its side. It's longer than a football field!

Inside the Main Hall of The Space and Rocket Center is an Apollo command module. This spacecraft went into orbit around the moon with three astronauts aboard. When it returned to Earth it made an ocean landing, called a splashdown. Handles on the outside helped the astronaut crew climb in and out.

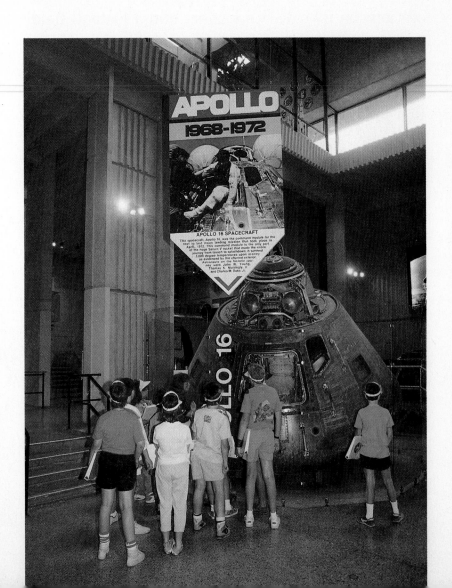

Not far from the command module stands a lunar module. This part of the craft separated from the command module during moon orbit. Two astronauts rode inside, down to the moon's surface. Also on board was the "moon buggy," which the astronauts drove. The gold foil helped to keep the inside cool by reflecting heat from the sun.

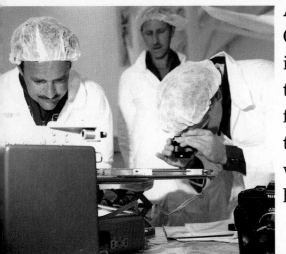

A short bus ride away from The Space and Rocket Center is the Marshall Space Flight Center. This is where NASA scientists and engineers help train astronauts, develop rockets, and plan for future space trips. Astronauts spend a lot of time training for their lab work in space. Important work on the Space Shuttle's rockets was also done here.

The Space Shuttle is different from earlier space vehicles. It takes off from Earth like a rocket, and travels through space like a spacecraft. Then it returns to Earth like an airplane. Going into space, it uses two solid rocket boosters and a huge external fuel tank. In Rocket Park, a mockup of the shuttle rests on its external fuel tank. A mockup is a full-size model that copies the shuttle in every detail.

Inside The Space and Rocket Center, many exhibits show the kinds of problems scientists must solve when planning for space travel. One exhibit shows two simple engines running inside a bell jar. When a button is pushed, all the air is removed from the jar, creating a vacuum. One engine stops because it cannot operate when there is no air. The other engine continues to run in the vacuum. This is the kind of engine that will operate in space.

Scientists also developed a special handling tool for astronauts to use in space. Visitors find that using this mechanical arm takes plenty of practice. Another exhibit lets visitors feel what it is like to steer a spacecraft. If not steered carefully, the craft will *pitch* (rock forward and back), *yaw* (wobble from side to side), or go into a *roll*.

Skylab was America's first space station. In the museum, visitors walk through sections of a Skylab mockup. Crews of three astronauts lived on board while Skylab orbited the earth for as long as three months. Since they were weightless in space, the astronauts could float from one area to another. Stairs weren't necessary.

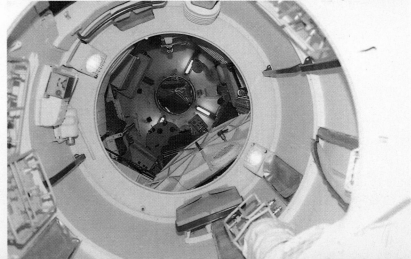

The mockup is an important part of space planning. Before each launch, scientists and engineers work inside it, using every piece of equipment again and again. They carry out all the activities the astronauts will repeat later in space. They have to be sure that they have remembered everything. When you go into space, there's no going back for what you forget.

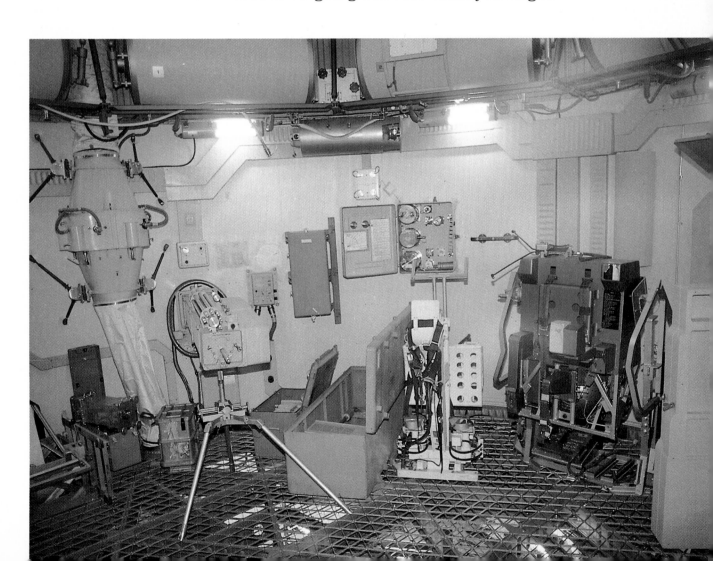

Every year, to find out more about going into
space, thousands of young people attend the U.S.
Space Camp® at The Space and Rocket Center. For
a few days they live like real astronauts and use
some of the same equipment astronauts use in
training. They even eat some of the same foods
astronauts eat on a space mission.

Students at the Space Camp are called trainees. One of the first projects for every trainee is to build and fire a simple rocket. This is a good way to learn how a rocket works. When the rocket fuel burns, it rushes out through the exhaust, pushing the rocket up into the sky. Tail fins guide the rocket on its short flight.

Trainees also get a good idea of what space travel feels like. For one thing, being weightless in space can be very confusing. It's hard to know where you are when there is no "up" or "down"! One machine used by the early astronauts gives the feeling of being in such an environment. Imagine what it is like to pitch, yaw and roll at the same time!

The *5DF chair* is another way to practice working in a weightless environment. 5DF stands for "five degrees of freedom" because the chair moves in five directions—forward and backward, side to side, in a forward spin, sideways like a cartwheel, and around like a top.

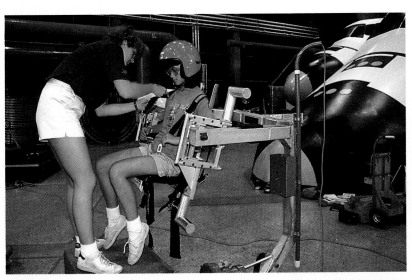

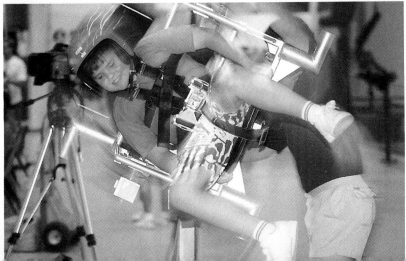

A ride on the moon-walk trainer lets a trainee feel the same gravity that astronauts feel when they are on the moon. Gravity on the moon is only one-sixth of what it is on the Earth. When astronauts walk on the moon they just bounce along.

One way to practice being in the weightlessness of space is to float in water. During training, astronauts dress in their space gear and, with floats attached, climb into a huge tank of water. There they test their equipment and practice the tasks they will carry out later in space.

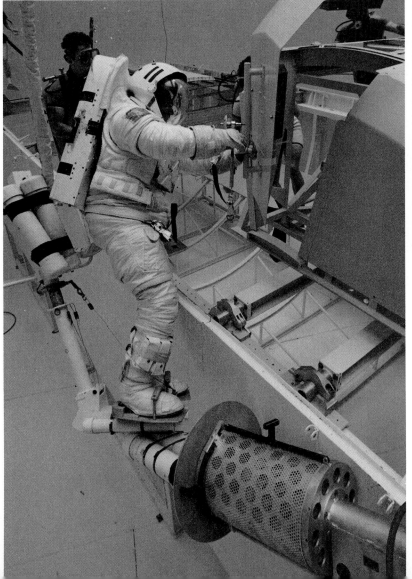

At Space Camp, youngsters practice being weightless in a swimming pool. They also learn what it is like to have a job to do in an unfamiliar environment. The simplest task can take special attention! One job is to load and unload a film can like the ones used aboard the Skylab.

"Suiting up" is a favorite camp activity. A space suit has both an inside layer and an outside layer. The inside layer looks like long underwear and is lined with tubes of liquid that control the suit's temperature. The outside layer is for protection. Without both layers, astronauts could not survive in space outside the spacecraft.

Suited up, a trainee gets to feel how hot and bulky the space suit is—and how *heavy*. A real astronaut's suit weighs 250 pounds! Worn with a helmet, it is a complete built-in life-support system. It provides oxygen for breathing and also maintains correct pressure around the body, protecting the wearer from the vacuum of space.

When astronauts are in space they may want to travel short distances away from their spacecraft. They can ride a special chair that is driven by small rockets. It lets them make repairs outside the spacecraft, or travel to a nearby satellite. Space trainees have a similar chair to ride. It "flies" a fraction of an inch above the floor.

Cooperation is the key to space travel. Nobody goes into space without the help of a support team back on Earth. Toward the end of Space Camp, everyone takes part in a simulated space mission. On the floor of the training center, groups of trainees divide into two teams. Members of one team play the roles of a shuttle crew, while the other team takes the job of Mission Control.

The day of the simulated flight is called Mission Day. As it begins, the youngsters playing members of the shuttle crew climb into a scaled-down model of the Space Shuttle. The *Commander* and the *Pilot* take their positions in the cockpit. Preparing for "liftoff," they go through the steps of their preflight check at the instrument panel.

As the countdown begins, everyone listens through headphones. At Mission Control the *Launch/Landing Director* is in charge of seeing that "all systems are go." If something does not check out, this is the person who can halt the mission. But the launch proceeds on course. Through the headphones, everyone soon hears the sound of the Space Shuttle leaving the Earth behind with a roar.

The job of the *Payload Specialist* is to carry out certain experiments on board the shuttle. He listens over the headphones as Mission Control tells the commander to cut off the main engines. When the shuttle settles into orbit around the Earth, the experiments can proceed in the area below the cockpit.

Behind the cockpit is the Payload Bay, where more experiments are done by *Mission Specialists.* On a real flight, the roof of this area is wide open during Earth orbit, and the crew works in the airless and weightless conditions of space. In the simulated flight, trainees ride 5DF chairs and have to handle some of the problems of being weightless. They practice building things with the same equipment future astronauts will use in space.

The job of one trainee is to transfer a gas from one container to another to see how weightless conditions affect the gas. This experiment copies one that the astronauts carried out on a real shuttle flight. On the simulated flight, the conditions of the test will appear on Mission Control's monitor screen, where a team member is waiting to record the results.

Soon the mission is almost over, and it is time for the shuttle crew to return to Earth. At Mission Control, the mission team checks the weather conditions. Low wind and good visibility are needed for the shuttle landing. All systems aboard the shuttle are checked to be sure everything is going exactly as planned.

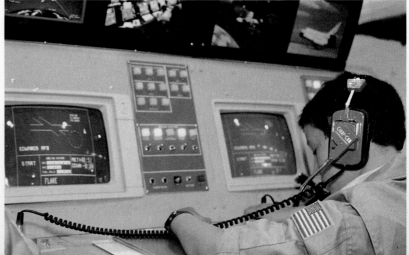

Soon the shuttle is ready to touch down. It's the end of a perfect flight. Or is it? Before the end of the mission, trainees may find a malfunction on board, or some other problem to handle. Finally, though, the crew makes a safe landing. Then counselors and trainees join in a *debriefing*. This means that everyone discusses what went well on the mission and what mistakes were made.

Space is very different from Earth. There is no other place quite as exciting. Someday perhaps you will pay a visit to a space station. Perhaps you will become a scientist or an engineer. You might even be an astronaut and have a job working in space!